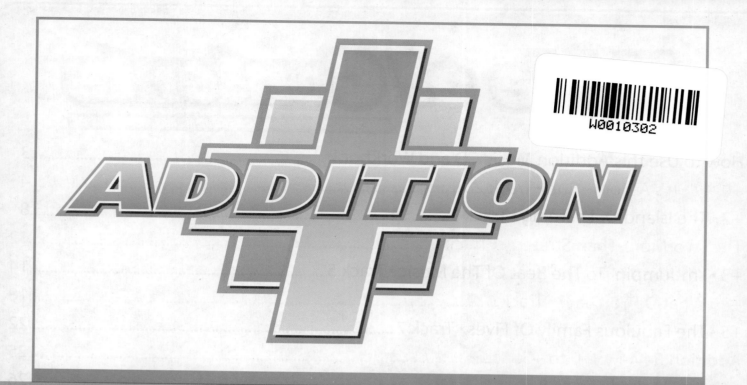

ADDITION

Twin 247CD
718451024727
ISBN-10: 1-57583-892-3
ISBN-13: 978-157583-892-2

Credits:

Publisher: Twin Sisters Productions, LLC
Executive Producers: Kim Mitzo Thompson, Karen Mitzo Hilderbrand
Music By: Kim Mitzo Thompson, Karen Mitzo Hilderbrand, Hal Wright
Music Arranged By: Hal Wright
Workbook Authors: Kim Mitzo Thompson, Karen Mitzo Hilderbrand, Ken Carder
Book Design: Steven Dewitt

www.twinsisters.com   1-800-248-TWIN(8946)

Table of Contents

How to Use This Addition Music CD and Workbook

Music makes learning fun and easy! We're confident that the songs and activities included in this 96-page Workbook and Music CD set will make learning addition a bit easier...and definitely a bit more fun.

The **original songs teach each fact 0 through 9** and several strategies that help many students better understand the concept of addition. The **lyrics to the songs are included** in this book. Encourage your child to listen to the music CD each day for a week or longer. Listen together in the car!

This workbook features **explanations, practice worksheets, learning games, and challenges** that can be played alone or with a partner—or even an entire classroom! Make photocopies of the pages for repeated practice. Many activities use the **10-sided dice** (page 95), that you can cut out and assemble in minutes.

Children should have addition, subtraction, multiplication, and division facts at their fingertips before they leave elementary school. For some, memorization comes easy. For others, memorization is much more difficult. In all cases, **memorization must follow an understanding of the concept**. Look for ways to count, combine, and sort objects. Look, too, for patterns and reasoning or strategies that help your child understand addition.

Listen and learn the songs together. Complete the worksheets and play the games together. Above all, enjoy the time together.

Words You Should Know:

ADDENDS: The numbers that are added. These numbers are also called TERMS.

ADDITION: To combine ADDENDS into one SUM.

SUM: The answer in Addition.

PLUS SIGN: + The symbol in a number sentence that tells you that you are supposed to add. When you read 2 + 3 you say, "Two plus three."

EQUAL SIGN: = The symbol in a number sentence that tells you that the numbers on either side have the same value. In 2 + 3 = 5, the number 5 has the same value as 2 + 3.

REGROUPING: To arrange a group differently

It's A Home Run

Be a home run hitter, be part of the team,
be a quick base runner, and you will succeed.
For if you practice hard in sports and school,
you will be a winner. Let determination rule!

Practice how to throw the ball,
practice how to catch,
and let your coaches teach you all the rest.
Math facts, fast balls, grounders, winning scores,
it's really all the same. Let's hear some more!

When you're adding zeros,
there's nothing you can do
but stay on that number.
Here's a little clue:
any number added to zero stays the same.
Let's practice this rule. It's an addition game.

0+1 is 1   0+6 is 6
0+2 is 2   0+7 is 7
0+3 is 3   0+8 is 8
0+4 is 4   0+9 is 9
0+5 is 5
(Chorus)

Now we're moving up.
Let's add the facts of one.
Another trick to learn.
We're having so much fun.
Take any number and then add one more.
You'll realize you count up one and no more.

1+1 is 2   1+6 is 7
1+2 is 3   1+7 is 8
1+3 is 4   1+8 is 9
1+4 is 5   1+9 is 10
1+5 is 6

(Chorus)

Once you know the rules
of a baseball game,
and strategies to help you
in adding–
I'll proclaim–practice makes
you better.
Yes, it's the only way.
So we'll mix up the facts,
and really concentrate.

1+8 is 9
0+5 is 5
1+3 is 4
0+7 is 7
0+2 is 2
1+9 is 10
1+1 is 2
0+8 is 8
1+2 is 3

(Chorus)

Zero "0" Strategy

Any number added to zero equals that number.

1 + 0 is 1	Think, "I have 1 and no more, only 1."
2 + 0 is 2	Think, "I have 2 and no more, only 2."
3 + 0 is 3	Think, "I have 3 and no more, only 3."
4 + 0 is 4	Think, "I have 4 and no more, only 4."
5 + 0 is 5	Think, "I have 5 and no more, only 5."
6 + 0 is 6	Think, "I have 6 and no more, only 6."
7 + 0 is 7	Think, "I have 7 and no more, only 7."
8 + 0 is 8	Think, "I have 8 and no more, only 8."
9 + 0 is 9	Think, "I have 9 and no more, only 9."

Count Up Strategy

If there is a 1, 2, or 3 in the problem, count up from the bigger number.

1 + 1 is 2	Think 1 and 1 more gives me 2.
1 + 2 is 3	Think 2 and 1 more gives me 3.
1 + 3 is 4	Think 3 and 1 more gives me 4.
1 + 4 is 5	Think 4 and 1 more gives me 5.
1 + 5 is 6	Think 5 and 1 more gives me 6.
1 + 6 is 7	Think 6 and 1 more gives me 7.
1 + 7 is 8	Think 7 and 1 more gives me 8.
1 + 8 is 9	Think 8 and 1 more gives me 9.
1 + 9 is 10	Think 9 and 1 more gives me 10.

Addition Practice: +0, +1

0	1	2	3	4	5	6	7	8	9
+ 0	+ 0	+ 0	+ 0	+ 0	+ 0	+ 0	+ 0	+ 0	+ 0

0	1	2	3	4	5	6	7	8	9
+ 1	+ 1	+ 1	+ 1	+ 1	+ 1	+ 1	+ 1	+ 1	+ 1

2	6	7	2	3	9	0	1	3	5
+ 1	+ 0	+ 0	+ 1	+ 0	+ 1	+ 1	+ 1	+ 0	+ 0

2	5	6	9	8	7	2	3	8	4
+ 0	+ 1	+ 0	+ 1	+ 0	+ 1	+ 1	+ 1	+ 1	+ 0

1	5	2	0	1	2	3	1	9	6
+ 4	+ 1	+ 0	+ 3	+ 0	+ 1	+ 1	+ 5	+ 1	+ 1

Around the Block

Race your partner around the block! Roll the 10-sided die. **Add either 0 or 1 to the number rolled**. Move your marker on the next space that matches that sum. The first player to reach home is the winner.

END		8	7	6	9	2	4
START	0	7	9	3	8	5	1
5	8	10	2	7	1	0	5
8	1	8	5	10	6	2	10
10	9	4	1	0	3	7	0
0	4	2	8	2	10	9	7
9	5	6	4	4	0	4	3
2	6	1	6	8	5	9	6
4	2	0	10	3	10	5	8
1	3	3	7	9	7	1	4
3	6	5	9	6	1	10	2

The Island Of Learning

Clap your hands and move with me
as we travel to the island of learning,
where adventure and knowledge you'll find.
It's a place that'll captivate your mind.

(Repeat)

It's time to do the limbo dance.
It's time to swing and move.
It's time to learn our facts of two
as we sing to the rhythmic groove.

2+1 is 3 and 2+2 is 4
Let us move the limbo stick
closer to the floor.

2+3 is 5 and 2+4 is 6
Gather as we do the dance
with our limbo stick.

(Chorus)

2+5 is 7 and 2+6 is 8
Bend your back and head real low.
Do not hesitate.

2+7 is 9 and 2+8 is 10
Now you've got the limbo down.
Let's do it all again.

2+9 is 11
Let's take it from the top and say our
facts as we do the dance
'til it's time to stop.

(Chorus)

2+1 is 3
2+2 is 4
2+3 is 5
2+4 is 6
2+5 is 7
2+6 is 8
2+7 is 9
2+8 is 10
2+9 is 11

(Chorus 2x)

Count-Up Strategy

If there is a 1, 2, or 3 in the problem,
count up from the bigger number.

2 + 1 is 3   Think, "I have 2 and 1 more. 3!"

2 + 2 is 4   Think, "I have 2 and 2 more. 4!"

2 + 3 is 5   Think, "I have 3 and 2 more. 5!"

2 + 4 is 6   Think, "I have 4 and 2 more. 6!"

2 + 5 is 7   Think, "I have 5 and 2 more. 7!"

2 + 6 is 8   Think, "I have 6 and 2 more. 8!"

2 + 7 is 9   Think, "I have 7 and 2 more. 9!"

2 + 8 is 10   Think, "I have 8 and 2 more. 10!"

2 + 9 is 11   Think, "I have 9 and 2 more. 11!"

0	1	2	3	4	5	6	7	8	9
+ 2	+ 2	+ 2	+ 2	+ 2	+ 2	+ 2	+ 2	+ 2	+ 2

2	2	7	2	2	9	0	2	2	5
+ 1	+ 0	+ 2	+ 1	+ 0	+ 2	+ 2	+ 1	+ 0	+ 2

2	5	2	9	2	6	2	3	8	2
+ 2	+ 2	+ 0	+ 2	+ 0	+ 2	+ 1	+ 2	+ 2	+ 0

2	2	6	7	2	9	2	2	1	2
+ 0	+ 1	+ 2	+ 2	+ 7	+ 2	+ 8	+ 0	+ 2	+ 6

1	2	2	0	2	2	5	2	9	6
+ 2	+ 1	+ 0	+ 2	+ 8	+ 7	+ 2	+ 5	+ 2	+ 2

Addition Bingo

Practice your addition facts +0, +1, +2 with a partner. Your partner rolls the 10-sided die, says the **number rolled, and "Add 0" or "Add 1" or "Add 2."** **Place a marker on the correct sum**. When you have five in a row, yell "BINGO!" For more fun, make your own Addition Bingo Cards so that you and your friends can play and practice your addition facts together!

B	I	N	G	O
1	10	5	3	11
7	3	9	4	6
4	1	0	11	8
9	5	10	2	5
3	8	2	7	1

The Two-More-Than Strategy

I'm going to teach you a simple strategy. When you're adding any number plus 2, just think "two-more-than" that number, or that number plus 2, and you will solve the problem easily. This is called the **two-more-than strategy**. Let's play a little game while we learn more about this strategy.

**It's the two-more-than, the two-more-than,
the two-more-than strategy.
It will help you add when one number is a two.
It's a wonderful plan. You'll see.**

Let's take a number—how about 3?–
and apply my simple rule.
Think "two-more-than" and what do you get? 5.
It's an awesome learning tool.

I say a number, and I want you to think
the two-more-than strategy.
Just move up two and you'll be right.
It makes learning fun indeed!

I say 6	think two more	6+2 is 8
I say 2	think two more	2+2 is 4
I say 7	think two more	7+2 is 9
I say 4	think two more	4+2 is 6

(Chorus)

I say 3	think two more	3+2 is 5
I say 8	think two more	8+2 is 10
I say 5	think two more	5+2 is 7
I say 9	think two more	9+2 is 11

If you see a problem and one number is a two,
just apply my simple rule.
Think "two-more-than" and the answer you'll know.
It's a wonderful learning tool.

(Chorus)

**It will help you add when one number is a two.
It's a wonderful plan. You'll see.**

Two-More-Than Strategy Game

Play this game with a partner. Race to be the first player to color or mark one entire "2". On your turn, roll the 10-sided die. Color or use a marker to mark the **sum** that is **2 more than the number rolled**. If no answer is left, your turn ends. Continue to play until one player marks or colors all the spaces on a "2". **Note: To play again and again, you may want to make photocopies of this page.**

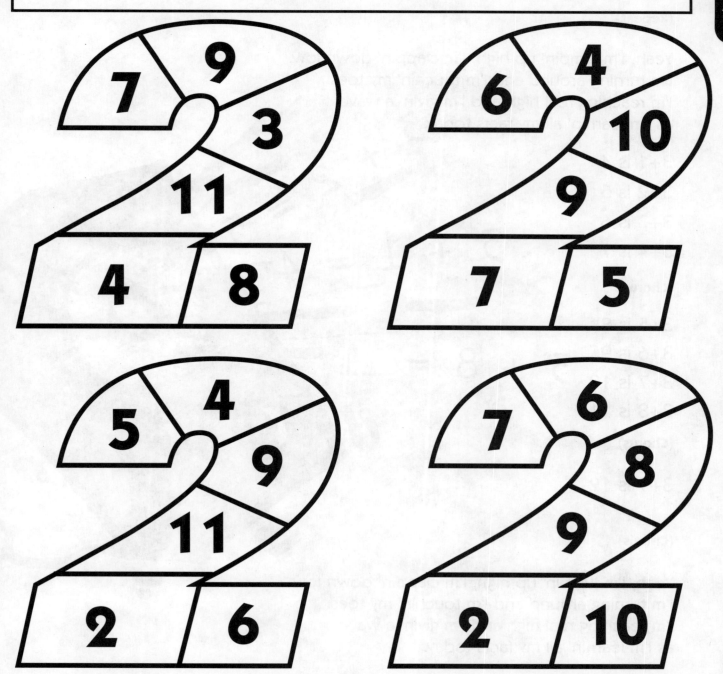

I'm Jumpin' To The Beat Of The Music

Addition: +3

I'm jumpin' to the beat of the music.
I'm jumpin' to the beat of the song.
Yeah, I'm jumpin' to the beat of the music.
Won't you come with me and jump along?

(Repeat)

Yeah, I'm jumpin' up high, I'm clappin' down low.
I'm turning around and I'm touchin' my toes.
I'm reaching real high and I'm givin' a wave
as I'm learnin' all my facts today.

3+1 is 4
3+2 is 5
3+3 is 6
3+4 is 7

(Chorus)

3+5 is 8
3+6 is 9
3+7 is 10
3+8 is 11

(Chorus)

3+9 is 12

(Chorus)

Yeah, I'm jumpin' up high, I'm clappin' down low.
I'm turning around and I'm touchin' my toes.
I'm reaching real high and I'm givin' a wave
as I'm learnin' all my facts today.

Jumpin' to the beat of the music.

Count Up Strategy

If there is a 1, 2, or 3 in the problem,
count up from the bigger number.

3 + 1 is 4   Think, "I have 3 and 1 more. 4!"

3 + 2 is 5   Think, "I have 3 and 2 more. 5!"

3 + 3 is 6   Think, "I have 3 and 3 more. 6!"

3 + 4 is 7   Think, "I have 4 and 3 more. 7!"

3 + 5 is 8   Think, "I have 5 and 3 more. 8!"

3 + 6 is 9   Think, "I have 6 and 3 more. 9!"

3 + 7 is 10   Think, "I have 7 and 3 more. 10!"

3 + 8 is 11   Think, "I have 8 and 3 more. 11!"

3 + 9 is 12   Think, "I have 9 and 3 more. 12!"

0	1	2	3	4	5	6	7	8	9
+3	+3	+3	+3	+3	+3	+3	+3	+3	+3

2	6	7	3	3	9	0	3	3	3
+3	+3	+3	+1	+0	+3	+3	+3	+8	+2

3	5	2	9	3	3	2	3	8	3
+2	+3	+3	+3	+0	+1	+3	+2	+3	+9

3	3	6	7	3	9	3	2	3	3
+0	+2	+3	+3	+7	+3	+8	+3	+2	+6

3	3	2	0	3	3	5	3	9	6
+2	+1	+3	+3	+8	+7	+3	+5	+3	+3

Target Practice

Complete the targets by adding the **addends** and writing the **sum** in the outer circle.

What Do You Say?

What do you say?
What do you say?

What do you say?
What do you say?
Let's learn our facts.
You'll be amazed.
What do you say?
What do you say?
Come, let's practice your facts today.

4+1 is 5   4+6 is 10
4+2 is 6   4+7 is 11
4+3 is 7   4+8 is 12
4+4 is 8   4+9 is 13
4+5 is 9

What do you say?
What do you say?
Let's learn our facts.
Now do you dare?
What do you say?
What do you say?
Come, let's practice—and be prepared.

4+1 is 5   4+6 is 10
4+2 is 6   4+7 is 11
4+3 is 7   4+8 is 12
4+4 is 8   4+9 is 13
4+5 is 9

What do you say?
What do you say?
Let's mix up the facts
before we start.
What do you say?
What do you say?
Shout the answers.
I know you're smart.

4+3 is...
4+9 is...
4+6 is...
4+7 is...

What do you say?
What do you say?
Are you ready for more?
Can you add today?
What do you say?
What do you say?
Shout the answers,
now don't delay.

4+9 is...
4+2 is...
4+5 is...
4+8 is...

What do you say?
What do you say?
You learned the 4s—
an accomplishment!
What do you say?
What do you say?
You are truly magnificent!

What do you say?

18

Number Line Addition

Write the missing **addend**. Finish drawing each problem on the number line.

Addition: +4

0 1 2 3 4 5 6 7 8 9 10 11 12 13

4 + __6__ = 10

0 1 2 3 4 5 6 7 8 9 10 11 12 13

4 + ____ = 7

0 1 2 3 4 5 6 7 8 9 10 11 12 13

4 + ____ = 10

0 1 2 3 4 5 6 7 8 9 10 11 12 13

4 + ____ = 5

0 1 2 3 4 5 6 7 8 9 10 11 12 13

4 + ____ = 8

0 1 2 3 4 5 6 7 8 9 10 11 12 13

4 + ____ = 4

0 1 2 3 4 5 6 7 8 9 10 11 12 13

4 + ____ = 11

0 1 2 3 4 5 6 7 8 9 10 11 12 13

4 + ____ = 13

0 1 2 3 4 5 6 7 8 9 10 11 12 13

4 + ____ = 12

0	1	2	3	4	5	6	7	8	9
+ 4	+ 4	+ 4	+ 4	+ 4	+ 4	+ 4	+ 4	+ 4	+ 4

4	2	7	4	4	9	0	7	4	5
+ 1	+ 4	+ 4	+ 4	+ 0	+ 4	+ 4	+ 4	+ 6	+ 4

2	4	4	9	4	4	4	4	8	4
+ 4	+ 2	+ 8	+ 4	+ 4	+ 7	+ 3	+ 5	+ 4	+ 0

4	4	6	7	2	9	4	4	4	4
+ 9	+ 7	+ 4	+ 4	+ 4	+ 4	+ 8	+ 0	+ 2	+ 6

3	4	2	4	4	4	5	4	9	6
+ 4	+ 1	+ 4	+ 7	+ 8	+ 7	+ 4	+ 5	+ 4	+ 4

Rhyme Time!

Add the **addends** then write a word that rhymes with each **sum**.

4 + 0 = _4_

Score

---

4 + 3 = ___

_____

---

1 + 4 = ___

_____

---

6 + 4 = ___

_____

---

2 + 4 = ___

_____

---

4 + 5 = ___

_____

---

4 + 7 = ___

_____

---

9 + 4 = ___

_____

---

8 + 4 = ___

_____

---

0 + 4 = ___

_____

---

4 + 4 = ___

_____

---

4 + 6 = ___

_____

---

3 + 4 = ___

_____

---

4 + 2 = ___

_____

---

4 + 9 = ___

_____

---

0 + 6 = ___

_____

---

7 + 4 = ___

_____

---

4 + 9 = ___

_____

---

4 + 1 = ___

_____

---

5 + 4 = ___

_____

Can you make a silly tongue twister or poem with the words?

_____

_____

_____

_____

_____

The Fabulous Family Of 5's

When you are learning addition facts, the numbers to be added together are called **addends**. The answer is called the **sum**. You can change the order of the addends around, but the sum will remain the same.

You can change the addends all around;
the sum remains the same.
You can add two numbers any which way;
the answer still remains the same.

Let's say the facts of five and then
we'll change the numbers around.
We'll learn our fabulous fives.
They're the coolest thing in town.

**It's the fab, fab, fab, fab,
fabulous family of fives.
Fabulous family of fives.
It's the fab, fab, fab, fab,
fabulous family of fives.
Fabulous family of fives.
We are featuring the friendly,
famously fine,
fan, fantastic, enthusiastic,
fab, fab, fab, fab,
fabulous family of fives.
Fabulous family of fives.**

5+1 is 6
5+2 is 7
5+3 is 8
5+4 is 9
5+5 is 10

Let's say the facts of five and then
we'll change the numbers around.
We'll learn our fabulous fives.
They're the coolest thing in town.

1+5 is 6
2+5 is 7

3+5 is 8
4+5 is 9
5+5 is 10

(Chorus)

You can change
the addends all around;
the sum remains the same.
You can add two numbers
any which way;
the answer still remains the same.

Let's move up to the higher facts,
then we'll change
the numbers around.
We'll learn our fabulous fives.
They're the coolest thing in town.

(Chorus)

5+6 is 11
5+7 is 12
5+8 is 13
5+9 is 14

Let's say the facts of five
and then we'll change
the numbers around.
We'll learn our fabulous fives.
They're the coolest thing in town.

6+5 is 11
7+5 is 12
8+5 is 13
9+5 is 14

(Chorus)

5 SEARCH!

Find and circle the facts of five! The **addends** and **sums** may be horizontal or vertical, forward or backward.

5 + 1 = ___	5 + 5 = ___	5 + 3 = ___	5 + 9 = ___	7 + 5 = ___
4 + 5 = ___	2 + 5 = ___	5 + 8 = ___	5 + 0 = ___	5 + 6 = ___

5	+	1	=	6	8	14	12
2	4	+	5	=	9	1	0
3	4	5	+	5	=	10	6
14	13	10	0	8	9	1	2
2	+	5	=	7	6	11	8
0	9	+	5	+	9	=	14
9	6	3	7	5	1	6	6
14	5	=	13	=	8	+	5
11	1	8	2	12	3	5	4

0	1	2	3	4	5	6	7	8	9
+ 5	+ 5	+ 5	+ 5	+ 5	+ 5	+ 5	+ 5	+ 5	+ 5

5	2	7	5	5	9	0	7	5	5
+ 1	+ 5	+ 5	+ 4	+ 0	+ 5	+ 5	+ 5	+ 6	+ 5

2	5	5	9	5	5	5	5	8	5
+ 5	+ 2	+ 8	+ 5	+ 4	+ 7	+ 3	+ 5	+ 5	+ 0

5	5	5	4	7	2	5	5	5	5
+ 9	+ 7	+ 6	+ 5	+ 5	+ 5	+ 8	+ 0	+ 2	+ 6

5	5	2	5	5	5	5	5	9	6
+ 3	+ 1	+ 5	+ 7	+ 8	+ 7	+ 5	+ 5	+ 5	+ 5

24

2	5	5	9	5	5	0	3	3	7
+ 5	+ 2	+ 8	+ 5	+ 4	+ 7	+ 3	+ 2	+ 6	+ 3

3	9	3	2	3	3	2	4	4	9
+ 7	+ 3	+ 8	+ 3	+ 2	+ 6	+ 4	+ 2	+ 8	+ 4

4	4	4	4	8	4	3	5	2	9
+ 4	+ 7	+ 3	+ 5	+ 4	+ 0	+ 2	+ 3	+ 3	+ 3

3	3	2	3	8	3	2	5	2	9
+ 0	+ 1	+ 3	+ 2	+ 3	+ 9	+ 2	+ 5	+ 2	+ 2

1	2	2	0	2	9	0	1	3	5
+ 2	+ 1	+ 0	+ 2	+ 8	+ 1	+ 1	+ 1	+ 0	+ 0

I'm Hooked

I am hooked on learnin'.
I am hooked on math.
I am hooked on learnin' my addition facts.
I'm feelin' kind of brainy 'cause I'm doing my part
to learn my 6s.
Now I'm hooked on being smart!

6+1 is 7
6+2 is 8
6+3 is 9
6+4 is 10
6+5 is 11
6+6 is 12
6+7 is 13
6+8 is 14
6+9 is 15

(Chorus)

Now I'm hooked on being smart!
Now I'm hooked on being smart!
Now I'm hooked on being smart!

I'm hooked!

I am hooked on learnin'.
I'll tell it to you straight.
If you study real hard and you concentrate.
Are you feelin' kind of brainy?
Are you ready to start?
Let's learn the 6s.
Now get hooked on being smart!

6+1 is 7
6+2 is 8
6+3 is 9
6+4 is 10
6+5 is 11
6+6 is 12
6+7 is 13
6+8 is 14
6+9 is 15

Counting the Blocks!

Count the blocks and write the **addends**. Find the **sum.**

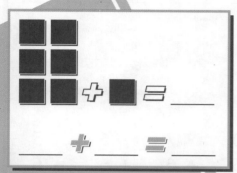

+ ___

___ + ___ = ___

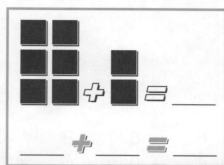

+ ___

___ + ___ = ___

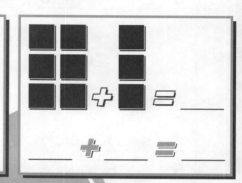

= ___

___ + ___ = ___

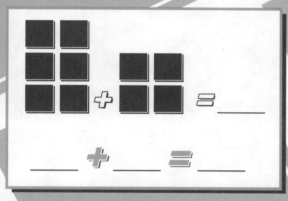

= ___

___ + ___ = ___

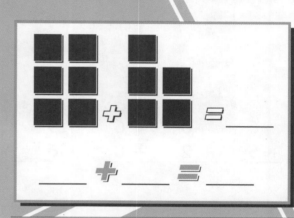

= ___

___ + ___ = ___

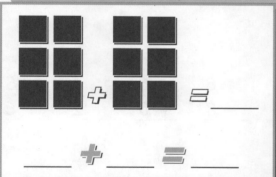

= ___

___ + ___ = ___

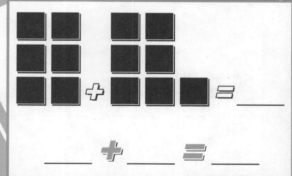

= ___

___ + ___ = ___

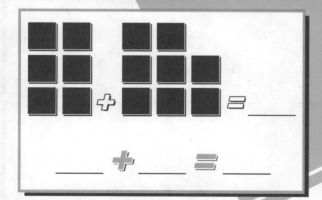

= ___

___ + ___ = ___

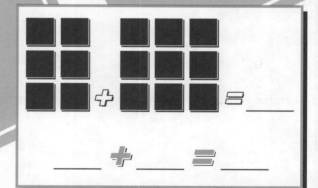

= ___

___ + ___ = ___

Addition Practice: +6

0	1	2	3	4	5	6	7	8	9
+ 6	+ 6	+ 6	+ 6	+ 6	+ 6	+ 6	+ 6	+ 6	+ 6

5	2	7	6	6	9	0	7	6	5
+ 6	+ 6	+ 6	+ 4	+ 0	+ 6	+ 6	+ 6	+ 6	+ 6

6	6	6	9	6	6	6	5	8	6
+ 5	+ 2	+ 8	+ 6	+ 4	+ 7	+ 3	+ 6	+ 6	+ 0

6	6	6	6	7	6	6	6	6	5
+ 9	+ 7	+ 6	+ 5	+ 6	+ 6	+ 8	+ 0	+ 2	+ 6

6	6	2	6	6	6	6	6	9	6
+ 3	+ 1	+ 6	+ 7	+ 8	+ 7	+ 5	+ 2	+ 6	+ 6

Counting the Blocks!

Play this simple game with a friend and practice the facts of six. You'll need the 10-sided die and several markers—buttons, candies, pennies or other game pieces—for each player. On your turn, roll the die and **add six to the number rolled.** Find and mark the correct **sum**. The winner is the first player to cover three squares in a row across, down, or diagonally.

6	15	10	12	9	14
9	7	13	7	12	11
8	12	8	11	10	14
7	13	14	9	12	6
12	9	8	15	10	13
11	13	7	14	8	11
15	10	14	15	6	13
8	12	9	6	11	7

Over And Over And Over Again

Addition: +1

**Over and over and over again.
Over and over and over and then
we'll learn our facts—if we repeat each
one over and over again.
(Repeat)**

7+1 is 8
7+2 is 9
7+3 is 10
Let's say them over and over again.

7+1 is 8
7+2 is 9
7+3 is 10
You won't hear the answers,
but say them again.

7+1 is...
7+2 is...
7+3 is...

(Chorus)

7+4 is 11
7+5 is 12
7+6 is 13
Let's say them over and over again.

7+4 is 11
7+5 is 12
7+6 is 13
You won't hear the answers,
but say them again.

7+4 is...
7+5 is...
7+6 is...

(Chorus)

7+7 is 14
7+8 is 15
7+9 is 16
Let's say them over and over again.

7+7 is 14
7+8 is 15
7+9 is 16
You won't hear the answers,
but say them again.

7+7 is...
7+8 is...
7+9 is...

(Chorus 2x)

**Over and over again.
Over and over again.**

Addition Practice: +7

0 + 7	1 + 7	2 + 7	3 + 7	4 + 7	5 + 7	6 + 7	7 + 7	8 + 7	9 + 7
5 + 7	7 + 6	7 + 7	7 + 4	7 + 0	9 + 7	0 + 7	7 + 7	7 + 6	5 + 7
6 + 7	7 + 2	7 + 7	9 + 7	7 + 6	7 + 4	6 + 7	5 + 7	8 + 7	7 + 0
7 + 9	7 + 7	6 + 7	7 + 6	7 + 6	7 + 9	7 + 8	0 + 7	2 + 7	7 + 2
7 + 3	7 + 1	2 + 7	6 + 7	7 + 8	7 + 7	5 + 7	6 + 7	9 + 7	7 + 7

Race a friend and practice your sevens, too! You'll need the 10-sided die and a marker—buttons, candies, pennies or other game pieces—for each player. On your turn, roll the die and **add seven to the number rolled.** Move your marker to the next space that matches the sum. The winner is the first player to reach the finish line!

END	13	14	16	12	9	7
START	8	16	8	14	7	16	10
7	10	11	12	11	11	14	8
10	12	13	11	7	9	8	15
16	16	7	16	110	13	7	14
8	13	9	14	9	16	11	16
13	14	12	7	16	8	13	12
7	7	15	15	13	7	15	11
11	8	7	9	8	10	9	13
16	16	10	11	7	12	12	9
9	11	8	16	15	9	10	7

Number Line Addition

Write the addition sentence shown on each line.

0 1 2 3 4 5 6 7 8 9 10 11 12 13 14 15 16

____ + ____ = ____

0 1 2 3 4 5 6 7 8 9 10 11 12 13 14 15 16

____ + ____ = ____

0 1 2 3 4 5 6 7 8 9 10 11 12 13 14 15 16

____ + ____ = ____

0 1 2 3 4 5 6 7 8 9 10 11 12 13 14 15 16

____ + ____ = ____

0 1 2 3 4 5 6 7 8 9 10 11 12 13 14 15 16

____ + ____ = ____

0 1 2 3 4 5 6 7 8 9 10 11 12 13 14 15 16

____ + ____ = ____

0 1 2 3 4 5 6 7 8 9 10 11 12 13 14 15 16

____ + ____ = ____

0 1 2 3 4 5 6 7 8 9 10 11 12 13 14 15 16

____ + ____ = ____

0 1 2 3 4 5 6 7 8 9 10 11 12 13 14 15 16

____ + ____ = ____

Addition: +8

We're learning our facts three at a time.
We're learning our facts while we exercise.
Get out of your seats. Let's run in place.
It's time to learn the facts of eight.

(Repeat)

8+1 is 9
8+2 is 10
8+3 is 11
Make sure to breathe that oxygen!

We're learning our facts three at a time.
We're learning our facts while we exercise.
Now, jumping jacks are next in line.
Look alive! I want everyone to try.

8+4 is 12
8+5 is 13
8+6 is 14
You're looking like a lean machine.

We're learning our facts three at a time.
We're learning our facts while we exercise.
Now, touch your waist and then your toes.
Down and up; yes, that's how it goes.

8+7 is 15
8+8 is 16
8+9 is 17
What a splendid learning scene.

We're learning our facts three at a time.
We're learning our facts while we exercise.
No books or pencils are needed today.
Follow my lead. I'll show you the way.

Now one more time.
I'm not ready to stop.
Up and at 'em.
Let's take it from the top!

(Chorus)

8+1 is 9
8+2 is 10
8+3 is 11
Make sure to breathe that oxygen!

We're learning our facts
three at a time.
We're learning our facts
while we exercise.
Now, jumping jacks are next in line.
Look alive! I want everyone to try.

8+4 is 12
8+5 is 13
8+6 is 14
You're looking like a lean machine.

We're learning our facts
three at a time.
We're learning our facts
while we exercise.
Now, touch your waist
and then your toes.
Down and up; yes, that's how it goes.

8+7 is 15
8+8 is 16
8+9 is 17
What a splendid learning scene.

We've learned our facts
three at a time.
We've learned our facts
while we exercised.
Jumping jacks, and we ran in place,
touched our toes,
now we know the eights!
(Repeat)

Search

Add the **addends** and write the **sum**. Find and circle each fact and write a + or = sign in the correct place.

8 + 1 = ___   8 + 5 = ___   1 + 8 = ___   3 + 8 = ___
8 + 9 = ___   8 + 3 = ___   9 + 8 = ___   2 + 8 = ___
8 + 7 = ___   8 + 2 = ___   7 + 8 = ___   0 + 8 = ___
8 + 6 = ___   8 + 0 = ___   6 + 8 = ___
8 + 4 = ___   8 + 8 = ___   5 + 8 = ___

9	8	0	8	11	1	8 + 1 = 9	0
5	2	7	8	6	14	13	7	6	7
1	10	9	16	3	9	8	17	12	8
8	6	8	14	1	8	12	17	13	15
4	5	2	3	0	1	13	6	8	14
12	8	7	15	11	5	0	3	5	7
2	3	5	9	8	5	13	0	1	14
17	11	13	1	6	0	16	8	9	17
5	9	2	8	10	5	3	8	11	9

0	1	2	3	4	5	6	7	8	9
+8	+8	+8	+8	+8	+8	+8	+8	+8	+8

8	8	2	8	8	9	0	8	6	8
+2	+0	+8	+1	+8	+8	+8	+1	+8	+5

7	5	8	8	2	8	5	3	8	2
+8	+8	+0	+2	+8	+1	+8	+8	+8	+8

0	2	8	7	8	9	8	8	8	8
+8	+8	+6	+8	+7	+8	+8	+0	+2	+6

1	2	8	8	8	7	5	8	9	6
+8	+8	+0	+2	+8	+8	+8	+5	+8	+8

Sequences

Review the addition facts 0 to 8 with a friend. The object of the game is to have two sequences of four markers in a row—up, down, or diagonally. To play, you'll need the 10-sided die and different markers—buttons, candies, pennies or other game pieces—for each player. On your turn, roll the die and **add any number 0 to 8 to the number rolled**. Say the problem out loud and **place a marker on the correct sum**. You'll need to watch the board and carefully choose your addition facts to stop another player from making a sequence.

1	9	17	1	8	14	2	6	9	11
11	2	8	16	2	9	15	3	7	10
4	12	3	7	15	3	10	16	4	8
14	5	13	4	6	14	4	11	17	5
7	15	6	14	5	5	13	5	12	1
16	8	16	7	15	6	4	12	6	13
7	17	9	17	8	16	7	3	11	7
14	8	1	10	1	9	17	8	2	10
3	15	9	2	11	2	10	1	9	1
8	4	16	10	3	12	3	11	2	10
12	9	5	17	11	4	13	4	12	3
15	13	10	6	1	12	5	14	5	13
17	16	14	11	7	2	13	6	15	6

It's Time To Review

The facts of nine we've really gone through.
So I think, by now, it is time to review.
We know our facts from 0-8.
The nines are last. Isn't that great?

It's time to review.
It's time to review.
For we know the facts, isn't it true?
Addition is easy if we strategize.
Learning the rules helps us memorize.

9+1 is 10
9+2 is 11
9+3 is 12
9+4 is 13
9+5 is 14
9+6 is 15
9+7 is 16
9+8 is 17

One more fact, and I'll say it now.
It's 9+9, which is 18. Wow!

The facts of nine are easy to know.
Say them again—and we'll take it slow.
We know our facts from 0-8.
The nines are last. Isn't that great?

(Chorus)

9+1 is 10
9+2 is 11
9+3 is 12
9+4 is 13
9+5 is 14
9+6 is 15
9+7 is 16

9+8 is 17

One more fact, and I'll say it now.

It's 9+9, which is 18. Wow!

(Chorus)

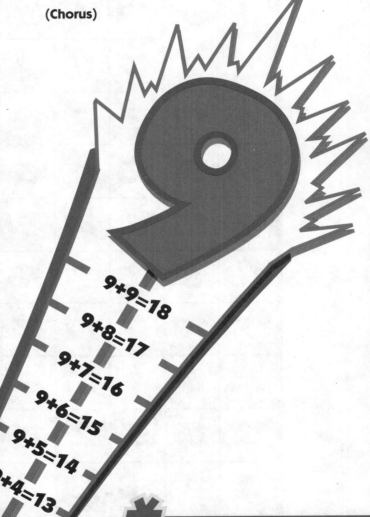

9+9=18
9+8=17
9+7=16
9+6=15
9+5=14
9+4=13
9+3=12
9+2=11
9+1=10

USING 10 TO ADD 9:
To help add 9 to a number, just add 10 to the number, and then subtract 1.

 38

Secret Code

Add the **addends**. Match the letter and the **sum** in the code to solve the riddle.

Code

T	O	S	I	E	U	H	!	D
10	11	12	13	14	15	16	17	18

What side of the chicken do feathers grow on?

1	9	5
+9	+7	+9

2	6	1	9	4	9	9	8
+9	+9	+9	+3	+9	+9	+5	+9

0 + 9	1 + 9	2 + 9	3 + 9	4 + 9	5 + 9	6 + 9	7 + 9	8 + 9	9 + 9
2 + 9	9 + 0	7 + 9	2 + 9	9 + 0	9 + 9	9 + 2	9 + 1	7 + 9	9 + 5
2 + 9	9 + 8	9 + 2	9 + 9	9 + 0	9 + 1	5 + 9	3 + 9	8 + 9	9 + 0
0 + 9	9 + 2	9 + 6	7 + 9	9 + 7	9 + 2	9 + 8	2 + 9	9 + 1	9 + 6
9 + 2	9 + 1	5 + 9	0 + 9	2 + 9	9 + 7	5 + 9	9 + 5	9 + 9	9 + 2

Round and Round

How fast can you make it to the center? Say the sum of each problem, moving from start to center! **Time Yourself!**

41

Addition: Doubles

I'm talkin' 'bout doubles.
Now, doubles mean two.
Doubles, doubles, doubles.
I'm tellin' the truth.

If you learn about doubles
when you're learnin' to add,
you'll ace all your tests
and make your teacher glad.

Doubles, doubles, doubles.
Now, doubles mean two.
Doubles, doubles, doubles,
doubles help you.
They'll help you learn quickly.
There are ten double facts.
Doubles, doubles, doubles.
We're talkin' doubly good math!

Let's take 1 and double it.   2
Let's take 2 and double it.   4
Let's take 3 and double it.   6
Let's take 4 and double it.   8
Let's take 5 and double it.   10
Now we'll say our facts all over again.

1+1 is 2
2+2 is 4
3+3 is 6
4+4 is 8
5+5 is 10

(Chorus)

Let's take 6 and double it.   12
Let's take 7 and double it.   14
Let's take 8 and double it.   16
Let's take 9 and double it.   18

Let's take 10 and double it.   20
You've got the idea.
You're learnin' plenty.

6+6 is 12
7+7 is 14
8+8 is 16
9+9 is 18
10+10 is 20

(Chorus)

I'm talkin' 'bout doubles.
Now, doubles mean two.
Doubles, doubles, doubles.
I'm tellin' the truth.

Let's mix up the doubles.
You can do the math.
Doubles, doubles, doubles.
We're learnin' the facts.

3+3 is 6
6+6 is 12
9+9 is 18
1+1 is 2
7+7 is 14
5+5 is 10
2+2 is 4
10+10 is 20
8+8 is 16
4+4 is 8

(Chorus 2x)

Now I'm Talkin' About Doubles Strategy

$1 + 1 =$ _____ $4 + 4 =$ _____ $7 + 7 =$ _____

$2 + 2 =$ _____ $5 + 5 =$ _____ $8 + 8 =$ _____

$3 + 3 =$ _____ $6 + 6 =$ _____ $9 + 9 =$ _____

Practice your doubles by saying, "One doubled is Two." See how quickly you can say the doubles one through nine this way! Have someone time you!

Study the sums of the doubles above. What do all the doubles have in common? Turn this page upside down to learn the answer.

1 DOUBLED IS 2!

2 DOUBLED IS 4!

3 DOUBLED IS 6!

4 DOUBLED IS 8!

5 DOUBLED IS 10!

6 DOUBLED IS 12!

7 DOUBLED IS 14!

8 DOUBLED IS 16!

9 DOUBLED IS 18!

Answer! All double facts are even numbers—always!

Addition Practice: Doubles

0	1	2	3	4	5	6	7	8	9
+ 0	+ 1	+ 2	+ 3	+ 4	+ 5	+ 6	+ 7	+ 8	+ 9

0	1	2	3	4	5	6	7	8	9
+ 0	+ 1	+ 2	+ 3	+ 4	+ 5	+ 6	+ 7	+ 8	+ 9

2	6	7	2	3	9	0	1	3	5
+ 2	+ 6	+ 7	+ 2	+ 3	+ 9	+ 0	+ 1	+ 3	+ 5

2	5	6	9	8	7	5	6	8	4
+ 2	+ 5	+ 6	+ 9	+ 8	+ 7	+ 5	+ 6	+ 8	+ 4

1	5	2	0	9	2	3	4	9	6
+ 1	+ 5	+ 2	+ 0	+ 9	+ 2	+ 3	+ 4	+ 9	+ 6

Double Dash

How fast will you Double Dash to the center? The object of the game is to make it to the center square. You can play alone or with a partner. To play, you'll need a marker for each player and the 10-sided die. On your turn, roll the die, **double the number**, and move your marker to that sum!

0	18	16	14	12	10	8	6	4	2
2	0	2	0	18	16	14	12	10	0
4	2	4	10	8	6	4	2	8	18
6	4	6	12	2	0	18	0	6	16
8	6	8	14	4	★	16	18	4	14
10	8	10	16	6	16	14	16	2	12
12	10	12	18	8	14	12	14	0	10
14	12	14	0	10	12	10	12	18	8
16	14	16	2	4	6	8	10	16	6
18	16	18	0	2	4	6	8	14	4
0	18	0	2	4	6	8	10	12	2
2	4	6	8	10	12	14	16	18	0

Doubles + One

I want to teach you a strategy called "doubles plus one." If you know your double facts, like 2+2 and 6+6, you will find this strategy helpful. If you have a problem where one addend is one more than the other, you can think of doubles and add one more. Let's look at 3+4. In the problem 3+4, 4 is one more than 3. So double 3 and add 1. 3+3 is 6 and 6+1 is 7! That's it. Look at 4+5. Double 4 and add one more. 4+4 is 8 and 8+1 is 9. Great!

Doubles plus one.
Doubles plus one.
Double the smaller number
and then add one. How fun!
(Repeat)

1+2 is 3
Just double 1, which is 2,
and add one more. 3

2+3 is 5
Just double 2, which is 4,
and add one more. 5

3+4 is 7
Just double 3, which is 6,
and add one more. 7

4+5 is 9
Just double 4, which is 8,
and add one more. 9

(Chorus)

5+6 is 11
Just double 5, which is 10,
and add one more. 11

6+7 is 13
Just double 6, which is 12,
and add one more. 13

7+8 is 15
Just double 7, which is 14,
and add one more. 15

8+9 is 17
Just double 8, which is 16,
and add one more. 17

(Chorus)

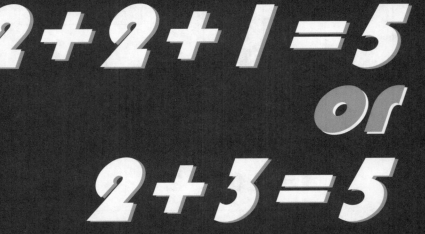

$$2+2+1=5$$
or
$$2+3=5$$

Doubles + One

Doubles Plus One: If you have a problem where one of the addends is one more than the other addend just double the smaller number and then add 1.

For example, 4 + 5:
We know that 5 is one more than 4. So, double the smaller addend 4, which is 8. Now, add one more which makes 9.

Practice using the "Doubles Plus One" strategy below.

3 + 4
Double 3 which is ____, and add one more, which makes _____   ___ + ___ = ___

6 + 7
Double 6 which is ____, and add one more, which makes _____   ___ + ___ = ___

3 + 2
Double ____ which is ____, and add one more, which makes _____   ___ + ___ = ___

5 + 4
Double 4 which is ____, and add one more, which makes _____   ___ + ___ = ___

3 + 2
Double ____ which is ____, and add one more, which makes _____   ___ + ___ = ___

8 + 9
Double ____ which is ____, and add one more, which makes _____   ___ + ___ = ___

5 + 6
Double ____ which is ____, and add one more, which makes _____   ___ + ___ = ___

8 + 7
Double ____ which is ____, and add one more, which makes _____   ___ + ___ = ___

6 + 8
Double ____ which is ____, and add one more, which makes _____   ___ + ___ = ___

9 + 8
Double ____ which is ____, and add one more, which makes _____   ___ + ___ = ___

Addition Practice: Doubles + One

1	2	3	4	5	6	7	8	0	2
+ 2	+ 3	+ 4	+ 5	+ 6	+ 7	+ 8	+ 9	+ 1	+ 1

4	5	6	7	8	1	3	7	8	5
+ 3	+ 4	+ 5	+ 6	+ 7	+ 2	+ 2	+ 6	+ 7	+ 4

0	1	2	3	4	6	1	5	6	9
+ 1	+ 2	+ 3	+ 4	+ 5	+ 5	+ 2	+ 6	+ 7	+ 8

3	6	7	5	4	5	3	8	7	6
+ 4	+ 5	+ 8	+ 6	+ 3	+ 4	+ 2	+ 9	+ 8	+ 5

1	5	7	1	7	3	6	3	7	4
+ 0	+ 6	+ 6	+ 2	+ 8	+ 4	+ 5	+ 2	+ 6	+ 5

Doubles + 1 Tower Race

The object of the game is to climb to the top of the tower the fastest! To play, set a kitchen timer for 30-seconds, 60-seconds or use a timer from another game. You'll each need a marker. Your partner quickly rolls the 10-sided die. You must **do the "double plus one" math**! Move your marker up the tower for each correct answer. Can you make it to the top of your tower before time runs out?

You can play this race against time with any addition fact, doubles, or even the "Doubles Plus Two" strategy on the next page!

Doubles + Two

Doubles Plus Two: When adding two numbers that are separated by one number, double the smaller number and add two.

For example: 4 + 6:
We know that 4 and 6 are separated by one number, 5. So, double the smaller addend which is 8. Now, add two more which makes 10

Practice using the "Doubles Plus Two" strategy below.

3 + 5
Double 3 which is ____, and add two more, which makes _____   ___ + ___ = ___

6 + 8
Double 6 which is ____, and add two more, which makes _____   ___ + ___ = ___

1 + 3
Double ____ which is ____, and add two more, which makes _____   ___ + ___ = ___

5 + 7
Double ____ which is ____, and add two more, which makes _____   ___ + ___ = ___

6 + 8
Double ____ which is ____, and add two more, which makes _____   ___ + ___ = ___

7 + 9
Double ____ which is ____, and add two more, which makes _____   ___ + ___ = ___

2 + 4
Double ____ which is ____, and add two more, which makes _____   ___ + ___ = ___

4 + 6
Double ____ which is ____, and add two more, which makes _____   ___ + ___ = ___

6 + 8
Double ____ which is ____, and add two more, which makes _____   ___ + ___ = ___

0 + 2
Double ____ which is ____, and add two more, which makes _____   ___ + ___ = ___

Mix 'N Match Addends

Check out how many ways you can you make 9 by adding just two addends!

1 + 8	3 + 6	2 + 7	9 + 0	4 + 5
8 + 1	6 + 3	7 + 2	0 + 9	5 + 4

Now, you try it!

With only two **addends**, see how many ways you can add up to...

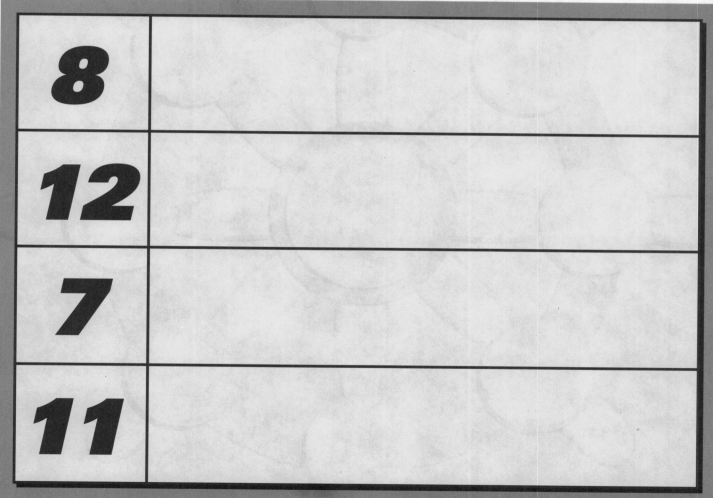

8	
12	
7	
11	

On another piece of paper, try using three addends!

Addition: Learning Games

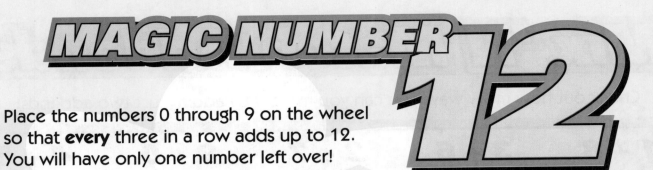

MAGIC NUMBER 12

Place the numbers 0 through 9 on the wheel so that **every** three in a row adds up to 12. You will have only one number left over!

Addition Table Race

Time yourself to see how quickly you can complete the addition table! Before completing the chart, you may want to photocopy the page so that you can practice many times! For more fun, play this game with one or more friends. The first player fills in any square on the addition table. The next player fills in another square. It is important to watch carefully what the other players write; if a player makes a mistake, another player may correct it on his or her turn. How quickly can you fill in all the squares!

+	1	2	3	4	5	6	7	8	9
1									
2									
3									
4									
5									
6									
7									
8									
9									

Addition: Learning Games

Calculator Race

The object of the game is to beat the calculator! You'll need three players. One player says an addition problem from the game board below. The second player solves the problem with the calculator. The third player solves the problem without a calculator. Player one decides who solved the problem first and places that player's initials in the box. Before playing, you may want to photocopy this page so you can play again and again.

0 + 0	0 + 1	0 + 2	0 + 3	0 + 4	0 + 5	0 + 6	0 + 7	0 + 8	0 + 9
1 + 0	1 + 1	1 + 2	1 + 3	1 + 4	1 + 5	1 + 6	1 + 7	1 + 8	1 + 9
2 + 0	2 + 1	2 + 2	2 + 3	2 + 4	2 + 5	2 + 6	2 + 7	2 + 8	2 + 9
3 + 0	3 + 1	3 + 2	3 + 3	3 + 4	3 + 5	3 + 6	3 + 7	3 + 8	3 + 9
4 + 0	4 + 1	4 + 2	4 + 3	4 + 4	4 + 5	4 + 6	4 + 7	4 + 8	4 + 9
5 + 0	5 + 1	5 + 2	5 + 3	5 + 4	5 + 5	5 + 6	5 + 7	5 + 8	5 + 9
6 + 0	6 + 1	6 + 2	6 + 3	6 + 4	6 + 5	6 + 6	6 + 7	6 + 8	6 + 9
7 + 0	7 + 1	7 + 2	7 + 3	7 + 4	7 + 5	7 + 6	7 + 7	7 + 8	7 + 9
8 + 0	8 + 1	8 + 2	8 + 3	8 + 4	8 + 5	8 + 6	8 + 7	8 + 8	8 + 9
9 + 0	9 + 1	9 + 2	9 + 3	9 + 4	9 + 5	9 + 6	9 + 7	9 + 8	9 + 9

Penny Addition

Count out 10 pennies and place them in the center of the table. One player grabs a few of the pennies. The second player takes the remainder of the pile. Both players count their pennies, secretly. The first player says how many pennies must be in the partner's hand. For example, "I have 6, so you must have 4." If correct, the player earns a point. If incorrect, the other player earns the point. Place all the pennies back in the center and play again. Change the number of pennies for a more challenging play.

Cereal Addition

Empty a box of cereal on a tray or in a baking pan. Say an addition problem. Count out the cereal pieces to find the sum.

Magic Dice

Roll two dice. What do the numbers add up to? For example, you roll a 1 and a 3 and the sum is 4. Without looking, do you know the sum of the bottom of those dice? Now, look. You'll see a 6 and a 4 with a sum of 10. Add the first sum and the second sum: 4 + 10 is 14.

Roll the dice again and follow the same steps. Do this several times. What pattern do you notice? Turn this page upside down to learn the pattern.

Hand-Clap Addition

With a partner, decide on a sum. For example, say you choose 12. The first player claps part of the sum: five times. The other player must then clap the rest of the sum: seven times. Take turns being the first partner.

CLAP! CLAP! CLAP! CLAP! CLAP!

CLAP! CLAP! CLAP! CLAP! CLAP! CLAP! CLAP!

+ =12

[Answer: With two dice, the magic number is fourteen. The tops and bottoms will always add up to fourteen. What's the magic number with three dice?]

License Plate Addition

The next time you're riding through town, try to add the "addends" you see in license plates. Some license plates have two, three, and even four numbers. Say the problem aloud and have someone check your answer! For more challenging play, first choose a sum. Everyone in the car then searches for a license plate with addends that equal that sum! You can also add up the addends in house numbers while you walk around the neighborhood!

PIG

You and a small group of friends will quickly pass the time—and practice your addition—with this classic game of strategy and chance. To play, you'll need a die, pencils, and paper. Take turns rolling a die and adding up your points. You can roll as many times as you want, but if you roll a 1, you lose all your points for that turn. When you choose to stop, write your score and pass the die to the next player. The first player to reach 100 points wins.

Addition WAR!

This twist on the classic card game, War, makes practicing addition facts even more fun! The game is played in much the same way the traditional card game is played. However, players add the cards they reveal. Each number card is worth its face value. The ace has a value of 1. You may want to remove the face cards. However, if you leave them in the deck, decide what values those cards might have. For example all face cards might have a value of 0 or 10; a jack might have a value of 10, a queen might have a value of 11, and a king might have a value of 12. Shuffle the deck of cards and place it face down. Each player draws a card from the top of the deck and reveals the card. Cards can be revealed one at a time or at the same time. When both cards are revealed, players must perform the assigned operation on the cards. For example, if one player flips over a 3 of diamonds and the other flips over an 8 of spades, then the players add in their heads the value of those two cards, $3 + 8 = 11$. The first player to call out "11" wins those two cards. Play until one player has all the cards!

56

Addition by the Cards

EXAMPLE:

How many ways can you add standard playing cards to total each number, 1 through 10? For beginners, add only two cards. For advanced play, add three cards. For more challenging fun, add four cards. To play, remove the face cards from a standard deck of playing cards. Place the cards on a table and explain your addition fact.

4
3 + 1
2 + 2
2 + 1 + 1 + 1

Capture the Cards

Two players try to capture the most cards. To play, remove the face cards from a standard deck of playing cards. Deal each player four cards and place the remaining cards face down. Place four cards face up in a row in the center of the table. On his or her turn, each player tries to capture as many cards as possible.

To capture a card:
- **Doubles**—match a card to a card on the table. For example, you have a 3 of diamonds in your hand and there is a 3 of hearts in the center. Capture both cards!
- **Table**—add two or more cards on the table that equal the value of one card in your hand. For example, if there is a 3 and a 2 in the center and you have a 5 in your hand, capture all three cards.
- **Hand**—add two or more cards in your hand that equal the value of one card on the table. If you have a 2, 3, and 4 in your hand and there is a 9 in the center, capture all four cards.

If you cannot capture any cards, discard one card from your hand and place it face up in the center. Whenever the center row runs out of cards, place two more cards from the deck face up to make a new row. Whenever a player runs out of cards, the player takes two more cards from the deck. The winner is the player with the most captured cards when no one can play another card.

3-Digit Addition Cards

Practice adding 3-digit numbers with a friend! Draw a 3 x 2 box on a piece of paper (3 boxes across and 2 boxes high). Remove the face cards and tens from a standard deck of playing cards. Shuffle the cards and draw the top card from the deck. Write this number in one of the boxes. Draw the next card from the deck and write that number in another box. Continue until all the boxes have been filled. Then add the two three-digit numbers. The player with the largest sum wins! For more fun, use a 3 x 3 grid and add three numbers!

Addition Tic-Tac-Toe

Play this challenging addition game while waiting at a restaurant or in a doctor's office. Draw a standard tic-tac-toe grid. Instead of using Xs and Os, players use the numbers 0 through 9. Each number can be used only once during a game. The object of the game is to complete any row, column, or diagonal so that two of the three numbers add up to the third number. The first move may NOT be in the center; the second and subsequent moves, however, can be anywhere on the grid.

Tic-Tac-15

Draw the traditional tic-tac-toe grid on a piece of paper. Take turns writing the numbers 0 through 9 in any square until the sum of three numbers in any vertical, horizontal, or diagonal row equals 15. Use each number only once! If no player reaches 15, begin a new game.

Addition Hide Away

The object of this challenging game is to be the first player to hide away all the markers. To play you'll need dice and at least 35 objects per player—candies, buttons, pennies, or other tiles. Players must first hide away two objects by rolling a sum of two with the dice. Players must then put away three objects by rolling a sum of three with the dice. The pattern continues until the player hides eight objects by rolling an eight. For more challenging play, use twelve objects. More advanced players may hide away the given number by subtracting or finding the difference.

Addition by the Bell

Challenge your classmates and practice your addition facts together with this noisy game! Ahead of time, write 25, 50, or more addition problems on index cards—one problem on each card—without the sum. Place the homemade flashcards face down on the table. You'll need a bell, buzzer, or some other noisemaker. To play, divide your friends into two teams. The first players from each team stand with their hands ready to ring the bell. You turn over the top addition problem card. As soon as a player knows the answer he or she rings the bell. The first student to ring the bell gets to say the answer; if correct he or she earns a point for the team. If a player hesitates or calls out the wrong answer, the other team receives the point. Play continues with the next two players. The first team to earn 25 or 50 points is the winner.

Beach Ball Addition

On the multi-colored sections of a beach ball write numbers 0 to 9. Toss the beach ball back and forth with a partner. When you catch the ball, you must add the numbers where your thumbs are before tossing the ball back to your partner.

Compare and write < (less than), > (greater than), or = (equal) in the circle.

6 + 3 ◯ 4 + 4

2 + 5 ◯ 8 + 2

9 + 4 ◯ 7 + 8

3 + 8 ◯ 5 + 5

2 + 7 ◯ 3 + 3

11 + 4 ◯ 12 + 3

10 + 3 ◯ 9 + 5

7 + 3 ◯ 6 + 2

3 + 4 ◯ 5 + 2

6 + 5 ◯ 5 + 7

8 + 1 ◯ 2 + 7

2 + 6 ◯ 7 + 2

2 + 2 ◯ 5 + 1

5 + 4 ◯ 6 + 3

2 + 3 ◯ 4 + 2

1 + 9 ◯ 5 + 5

8 + 3 ◯ 9 + 4

7 + 3 ◯ 11 + 0

5 + 5 ◯ 2 + 6

2 + 2 ◯ 1 + 3

8 + 4 ◯ 6 + 5

8 + 5 ◯ 7 + 6

9 + 0 ◯ 6 + 9

8 + 1 ◯ 5 + 2

*MORE < or > or =

Compare and write < (less than), > (greater than), or = (equal) in the circle.

7 + 9 ◯ 9 + 7	9 + 2 ◯ 5 + 6
6 + 5 ◯ 8 + 4	5 + 3 ◯ 6 + 3
4 + 3 ◯ 6 + 2	2 + 5 ◯ 4 + 4
2 + 9 ◯ 5 + 5	9 + 1 ◯ 5 + 5
7 + 5 ◯ 6 + 6	7 + 3 ◯ 9 + 2
9 + 8 ◯ 7 + 7	4 + 3 ◯ 6 + 0
6 + 1 ◯ 2 + 5	5 + 9 ◯ 8 + 6
7 + 3 ◯ 5 + 4	2 + 2 ◯ 1 + 4
6 + 4 ◯ 5 + 5	8 + 4 ◯ 6 + 6
3 + 2 ◯ 4 + 0	8 + 6 ◯ 7 + 8
8 + 1 ◯ 5 + 3	9 + 2 ◯ 6 + 9
2 + 6 ◯ 7 + 2	8 + 1 ◯ 5 + 3

The Missing Addend

Fill in the missing addends to complete the addition fact.

☐	☐	1	3	☐	7	☐	☐
+ 2	+ 9	+ ☐	+ ☐	+ 3	+ ☐	+ 6	+ 9
3	12	8	6	7	12	9	14

2	☐	6	3	2	7	☐	3
+ ☐	+ 5	+ ☐	+ ☐	+ ☐	+ ☐	+ 1	+ ☐
9	8	12	4	5	10	2	12

☐	☐	6	3	2	8	☐	2
+ 9	+ 8	+ ☐	+ ☐	+ ☐	+ ☐	+ 6	+ ☐
18	15	8	10	7	16	11	8

☐	☐	1	3	☐	5	☐	1
+ 2	+ 9	+ ☐	+ ☐	+ 8	+ ☐	+ 4	+ ☐
9	12	5	4	17	12	11	6

☐	☐	☐	☐	9	☐	3	5
+ 6	+ 9	+ 6	+ 4	+ ☐	+ 3	+ ☐	+ ☐
11	12	14	9	18	7	12	7

Three Addend Addition

Begin by finding the **sum** of the first two **addends**. Now, add the third **addend**.

$$5 + 2 + 6 = 13 \quad \bullet \quad \text{Think } 5 + 2 = 7 \quad \bullet \quad \text{Then } 7 + 6 = 13$$

Practice with these problems:

1. $6 + 3 + 7$

   $6 + 3 = \underline{\quad}$

   $\underline{\quad} + 7 = \underline{\quad}$

   $6 + 3 + 7 = \underline{\quad}$

4. $3 + 5 + 8$

   $3 + 5 = \underline{\quad}$

   $\underline{\quad} + 8 = \underline{\quad}$

   $3 + 5 + 8 = \underline{\quad}$

2. $4 + 5 + 6$

   $4 + 5 = \underline{\quad}$

   $\underline{\quad} + 6 = \underline{\quad}$

   $4 + 5 + 6 = \underline{\quad}$

5. $6 + 1 + 5$

   $6 + 1 = \underline{\quad}$

   $\underline{\quad} + 5 = \underline{\quad}$

   $6 + 1 + 5 = \underline{\quad}$

3. $2 + 4 + 8$

   $2 + 4 = \underline{\quad}$

   $\underline{\quad} + 8 = \underline{\quad}$

   $2 + 4 + 8 = \underline{\quad}$

6. $7 + 2 + 4$

   $7 + 2 = \underline{\quad}$

   $\underline{\quad} + 4 = \underline{\quad}$

   $7 + 2 + 4 = \underline{\quad}$

Three Addend Addition

3	6	5	2	8	4	2
2	5	1	3	2	5	5
+ 1	+ 1	+ 3	+ 6	+ 3	+ 8	+ 6

3	8	3	3	2	4	5
6	2	3	3	1	2	5
+ 7	+ 5	+ 3	+ 4	+ 7	+ 8	+ 6

7	4	3	2	7	4	1
2	5	1	3	2	0	5
+ 1	+ 1	+ 2	+ 2	+ 4	+ 8	+ 4

6	6	4	9	8	3	4
2	0	1	3	2	7	4
+ 1	+ 1	+ 4	+ 0	+ 3	+ 0	+ 4

7	4	9	6	4	3	1
2	5	1	3	2	2	8
+ 1	+ 2	+ 1	+ 6	+ 3	+ 7	+ 6

9	3	5	2	7	3	1
0	6	6	1	0	1	5
+ 1	+ 5	+ 3	+ 8	+ 9	+ 9	+ 9

Two-Digit Addends

36 is a two-digit number. Read a two-digit number from left to right. The first number tells you how many groups of ten are in the number. Practice skip counting by tens now!

The second number tells you how many ones are standing alone, waiting to join a group of ten.

Look at the number 36. The first digit is a 3 which means there are three groups of ten.
Skip count by tens 3 times and write the number here: _____.
The second number is a 6 which means there are 6 waiting to join a group of ten.

You try it ...

25 = _____ groups of ten + _____ waiting to join a group of ten.

42 = _____ groups of ten + _____ waiting to join a group of ten.

31 = _____ groups of ten + _____ waiting to join a group of ten.

27 = _____ groups of ten + _____ waiting to join a group of ten.

61 = _____ groups of ten + _____ waiting to join a group of ten.

58 = _____ groups of ten + _____ waiting to join a group of ten.

39 = _____ groups of ten + _____ waiting to join a group of ten.

44 = _____ groups of ten + _____ waiting to join a group of ten.

28 = _____ groups of ten + _____ waiting to join a group of ten.

35 = _____ groups of ten + _____ waiting to join a group of ten.

Advanced Addition

One- and Two-Digit Addends

Add the **ONES** in these two addends. Write the sum underneath the **ONES**.

$$
\begin{array}{r}
3\mathbf{1} \\
+\ \mathbf{5} \\
\hline
\underline{\mathbf{6}}
\end{array}
$$

Next, add the **TENS** in these two addends. Write the sum underneath the **TENS**.

$$
\begin{array}{r}
\mathit{3}1 \\
+\ 5 \\
\hline
\mathit{36}
\end{array}
$$

Practice by solving each problem:

41	56	73	14	21
+ 2	+ 3	+ 4	+ 5	+ 6

20	16	60	22	82
+ 6	+ 3	+ 9	+ 5	+ 6

63	82	91	14	61	31	12	80	10	42
+ 5	+ 3	+ 4	+ 3	+ 6	+ 8	+ 3	+ 9	+ 1	+ 4

35	56	60	52	21	18	73	51	15	55
+ 2	+ 3	+ 4	+ 5	+ 6	+ 1	+ 3	+ 7	+ 2	+ 1

54	27	14	61	42	23	41	21	37	12
+ 2	+ 2	+ 4	+ 7	+ 6	+ 5	+ 8	+ 4	+ 2	+ 6

61	81	28	32	22	10	52	35	70	43
+ 7	+ 3	+ 1	+ 4	+ 7	+ 8	+ 3	+ 4	+ 5	+ 6

25	61	71	33	21	80	36	12	22	21
+ 2	+ 8	+ 5	+ 5	+ 6	+ 9	+ 3	+ 6	+ 6	+ 5

Two-Digit Addends

```
  38      Add the ONES first.   8 + 1 = 9
+ 11      Then add the TENS.    3 + 1 = 4
----
  49
```

28 +11	40 +39	62 +34	12 +25	81 +17	71 +26	22 +33
50 +35	24 +51	49 +20	10 +34	29 +60	34 +21	26 +31
30 +40	62 +11	71 +20	44 +44	12 +14	68 +10	91 +18
28 +31	17 +22	34 +34	21 +47	19 +20	38 +11	17 +12
60 +29	71 +21	58 +20	14 +54	16 +13	26 +23	15 +13

Try adding this problem.

$$66$$
$$+18$$

First, **add the ones** and write the **sum** here: _____

Is the **sum** greater than 10 or less than 10? _____

The number 14 is the same as 10 + 4. Think of **1 group of 10** and 4 all alone. Give that **1 ten** to the **tens**. Now add the **tens**.

$$\overset{1}{}$$
$$66$$
$$+18$$
$$\overline{4}$$

$$\overset{1}{}$$
$$66$$
$$+18$$
$$\overline{84}$$

This strategy is called **REGROUPING**

Practice adding these two-digit numbers using **Regrouping.**

59	76	42	48	65	39	29
+28	+19	+39	+28	+19	+56	+19

Two-Digit Addends with Regrouping

| 48 | 28 | 29 | 36 | 57 | 27 | 33 |
| +17 | +18 | +23 | +16 | +19 | +54 | +29 |

| 66 | 15 | 77 | 24 | 88 | 39 | 29 |
| +18 | +28 | +15 | +27 | +13 | +44 | +32 |

| 52 | 37 | 82 | 66 | 27 | 68 | 43 |
| +29 | +26 | +29 | +25 | +39 | +24 | +28 |

| 22 | 53 | 48 | 65 | 79 | 32 | 18 |
| +69 | +19 | +24 | +18 | +12 | +29 | +29 |

| 72 | 47 | 18 | 68 | 78 | 55 | 63 |
| +19 | +18 | +23 | +15 | +13 | +16 | +19 |

| 23 | 16 | 32 | 57 | 54 | 28 | 36 |
| +79 | +18 | +28 | +27 | +39 | +34 | +47 |

Hundreds, Tens, and Ones

Three-digit numbers include groups of ONES, TENS, and HUNDREDS. The first digit tells how many groups of HUNDREDS. The middle number tells how many groups of TENS. The last number tells how many ONES.

473 = 400 + 70 + 3
473 = 4 hundreds + 7 tens + 3 ones

Read each sentence. Circle the correct numeral.

1. Circle the tens.   5   9   3

2. Circle the ones.   3   8   9

3. Circle the hundreds.   5   7   2

4. Circle the tens.   2   9   5

5. Circle the hundreds.   8   6   1

6. Circle the ones.   9   3   8

7. Circle the hundreds.   5   4   2

8. Circle the tens.   2   5   9

9. Circle the ones.   1   7   7

10. Circle the hundreds.   4   8   2

11. Circle the tens.   6   4   4

12. Circle the hundreds.   1   6   8

13. Circle the ones.   3   2   7

14. Circle the tens.   5   5   5

15. Circle the hundreds.   8   1   7

Three-Digit Addends

Try adding this problem:

$$
\begin{array}{r}
594 \\
+337 \\
\hline
\end{array}
$$

First **add the ones** and write the sum here: _____
Is the sum greater than 10 or less than 10? _____
11 is the same as 10 + 1. Think of it as **1 group of 10** and **1 all alone**.
Give that **1 group ten** to the tens.

$$
\begin{array}{r}
1 \\
594 \\
+337 \\
\hline
1
\end{array}
$$

Now add the tens and write the sum here: ____
Is the sum greater than 10 or less than 10? _____
Think of 13 groups of ten as **1 group of 100** plus **three groups of 10**.
Give the **1 group of 100** to the hundreds.

$$
\begin{array}{r}
11 \\
594 \\
+337 \\
\hline
31
\end{array}
$$

Now add the **hundreds** and write the sum here: ____

$$
\begin{array}{r}
11 \\
594 \\
+337 \\
\hline
931
\end{array}
$$

Practice adding these three-digit numbers using **Regrouping.**

| $\begin{array}{r} 323 \\ +588 \\ \hline \end{array}$ | $\begin{array}{r} 276 \\ +345 \\ \hline \end{array}$ | $\begin{array}{r} 189 \\ +256 \\ \hline \end{array}$ | $\begin{array}{r} 478 \\ +248 \\ \hline \end{array}$ | $\begin{array}{r} 529 \\ +184 \\ \hline \end{array}$ |

Advanced Addition

385 + 126	749 + 232	459 + 149	284 + 238	175 + 438
253 + 167	809 + 158	599 + 232	465 + 287	394 + 129
846 + 124	145 + 365	824 + 139	628 + 367	125 + 496
269 + 524	199 + 122	654 + 163	348 + 158	284 + 339
529 + 175	274 + 446	287 + 356	172 + 349	627 + 194

Real-Life Problem Solving

1 Christopher rode the rollercoaster 6 times. Anthony rode the roller coaster 4 times. How many times did they ride the rollercoaster altogether?

2 Eight adults rode the Ferris wheel. Ten children rode with them. How many people rode the Ferris wheel altogether?

3 Joshua and Phillip were fishing. Joshua caught 8 fish and Phillip caught 7 fish. How many fish did they catch altogether?

4 Emily has a large collection of stuffed animals. She has 8 teddy bears, 6 rabbits, and 4 puppies. How many stuffed animals does Emily have altogether?

5 Four third-grade classes are on the playground. Two second-grade classes and one third-grade class join them. How many classes are on the playground altogether?

6 Jason's father is grilling hamburgers for Jason and his sisters. Jason will eat two burgers and his three sisters will each eat one. How many hamburgers should his father grill altogether?

7 Amanda invited six girls from her class to a sleepover. She also invited six girls from her ballet class to the sleepover. How many girls did Amanda invite?

8 Tiffany's family lives on a farm. They have 7 brown horses and 4 black horses. How many horses do they have altogether?

9 Brad and four friends are planning to ride together to the skateboard park. Five other friends from school will also be there. How many friends will be at the skateboard park altogether? Remember to include Brad!

10 Jay rode his bike 8 miles. Austin rode his bike 7 miles. And Steven rode his bike 9 miles. How many miles did the three friends ride altogether?

Real-Life Problem Solving

1 Last month, Kyle used 76 minutes on his cell phone. Carrie used 87 minutes on her cell phone. How many minutes did Kyle and Carrie use altogether?

2 Jared's football team scored 21 points in the first half of the championship game. The team scored 14 points in the second half of the game. How many points did the team score in the championship game?

3 Nicole made a bead bracelet using 45 white beads and 32 gold beads. How many beads did she use altogether?

4 Eighteen boys and 14 girls registered for the soccer team last week. How many registered for the team altogether last week?

5 Sam's baseball team won 18 games this season and 17 games last season. How many games has the team won in both seasons?

6 Joey saved $25 he received for his birthday. He earned $15 by raking leaves. How much money does Joey have altogether?

7 Nathan has 18 music CDs in his room. His brother, Stephen, has 19 music CDs. How many music CDs do the boys have altogether?

8 Megan and Taylor were the candidates for president of their club. Megan received 14 votes and 16 voted for Taylor. How many club members voted?

9 Amanda practiced piano for 12 hours last week. This week she practiced 15 hours. How many hours did Amanda practice piano altogether?

10 The boys ate 44 hot dogs and 33 hamburgers. How many hotdogs and hamburgers did the boys eat altogether?

Real-Life Problem Solving

1 The video game store has 289 new games and 396 used games for sale. How many games does the store have for sale altogether?

2 To reach the ocean, Jacob's family drove 655 miles the first day of their vacation and 427 miles the second day. How many miles did they drive?

3 At Michael's school there are 128 first graders, 139 second graders. How many first and second graders are there altogether?

4 Taylor works at an ice cream stand. Last Saturday she scooped 177 dips of chocolate and 196 dips of vanilla. How many scoops of chocolate and vanilla ice cream did Taylor scoop last Saturday?

5 John lives with his family on a farm. His parents and grandparents farm 310 acres of corn and 626 acres of soybeans. How many acres do they farm altogether?

6 Kristen visited the school book fair. There were 265 nonfiction books and 155 fiction books for sale. How many books were for sale altogether at the book fair?

7 At the last swim meet, 129 boys and 118 girls competed. How many swimmers competed altogether in the meet?

8 At the zoo, one giant sea turtle weighs 476 pounds and its mate weighs 397 pounds. How much do the two sea turtles weigh together?

9 Lauren has 324 key chains in her collection. Her brother has 183 coins in his collection. How many items do Lauren and her brother have in their collections combined?

10 The students voted for their favorite food. 396 students voted for pizza and 122 voted for macaroni and cheese. How many students voted?

Time Test: +1, +2, +3, +4

1 + 2	4 + 3	5 + 2	6 + 4	3 + 2	7 + 2	6 + 3	5 + 1	9 + 1	8 + 2
7 + 3	5 + 4	6 + 2	1 + 4	3 + 1	5 + 2	3 + 2	8 + 4	7 + 2	9 + 2
0 + 1	3 + 4	3 + 3	2 + 4	5 + 4	7 + 1	4 + 2	6 + 4	6 + 2	8 + 3
7 + 4	6 + 1	8 + 2	3 + 4	9 + 3	5 + 4	4 + 2	2 + 4	1 + 3	6 + 4
1 + 4	4 + 4	7 + 4	3 + 2	2 + 3	3 + 4	9 + 4	8 + 2	5 + 4	6 + 3
3 + 2	4 + 6	9 + 2	6 + 4	2 + 8	4 + 7	2 + 6	5 + 1	9 + 3	7 + 2
6 + 3	2 + 4	5 + 2	1 + 3	9 + 1	7 + 2	2 + 2	4 + 4	6 + 2	9 + 2
1 + 1	3 + 9	4 + 3	2 + 3	8 + 4	7 + 4	3 + 4	6 + 3	6 + 1	3 + 7
7 + 2	8 + 3	5 + 2	3 + 8	3 + 3	5 + 2	6 + 2	2 + 6	5 + 3	8 + 4
5 + 4	3 + 4	7 + 1	5 + 2	2 + 9	6 + 4	8 + 4	8 + 2	2 + 4	6 + 2

76

1 + 5	4 + 7	5 + 6	6 + 8	3 + 6	7 + 7	6 + 9	5 + 5	9 + 8	8 + 7
7 + 6	5 + 5	6 + 9	1 + 7	3 + 8	5 + 6	3 + 5	8 + 7	7 + 6	9 + 5
7 + 5	6 + 7	8 + 6	3 + 9	9 + 8	5 + 7	4 + 5	2 + 6	1 + 8	6 + 9
1 + 8	4 + 5	7 + 7	3 + 8	2 + 7	3 + 6	9 + 9	8 + 6	5 + 5	6 + 7
6 + 5	7 + 7	5 + 2	6 + 6	8 + 6	7 + 9	6 + 4	6 + 8	2 + 8	4 + 7
4 + 9	5 + 8	7 + 7	4 + 8	5 + 9	9 + 9	3 + 5	8 + 9	6 + 6	9 + 2
1 + 9	3 + 7	3 + 9	8 + 5	7 + 7	7 + 6	3 + 5	6 + 5	5 + 8	8 + 9
2 + 8	4 + 8	3 + 7	8 + 8	6 + 7	3 + 5	9 + 9	5 + 6	7 + 5	9 + 7
3 + 2	4 + 6	9 + 2	6 + 4	8 + 2	4 + 7	2 + 6	5 + 1	9 + 3	7 + 2
1 + 2	4 + 3	5 + 2	6 + 4	3 + 2	7 + 2	6 + 3	5 + 1	9 + 1	8 + 2

3	7	1	3	3	5	6	9	9	6
+ 5	+ 7	+ 9	+ 8	+ 6	+ 7	+ 9	+ 5	+ 2	+ 7

4	5	3	2	3	4	3	9	4	5
+ 6	+ 3	+ 9	+ 7	+ 1	+ 6	+ 4	+ 7	+ 6	+ 5

0	3	4	2	9	8	4	6	6	8
+ 1	+ 8	+ 3	+ 0	+ 4	+ 1	+ 7	+ 6	+ 2	+ 3

7	6	8	3	2	5	4	7	1	6
+ 4	+ 8	+ 9	+ 4	+ 3	+ 6	+ 2	+ 4	+ 8	+ 4

3	9	5	6	3	4	6	5	7	9
+ 2	+ 3	+ 6	+ 6	+ 5	+ 2	+ 3	+ 8	+ 1	+ 5

7	5	6	1	3	5	3	8	7	9
+ 6	+ 5	+ 9	+ 7	+ 8	+ 6	+ 5	+ 7	+ 6	+ 5

7	5	6	1	3	5	3	8	7	9
+ 3	+ 4	+ 2	+ 4	+ 1	+ 2	+ 2	+ 4	+ 2	+ 2

6	7	5	6	8	7	6	6	8	4
+ 5	+ 7	+ 2	+ 6	+ 6	+ 9	+ 4	+ 8	+ 2	+ 7

1	4	5	6	3	7	6	5	9	8
+ 5	+ 7	+ 6	+ 8	+ 6	+ 7	+ 9	+ 5	+ 8	+ 7

7	5	6	1	3	5	3	8	7	9
+ 6	+ 5	+ 9	+ 7	+ 8	+ 6	+ 5	+ 7	+ 6	+ 5

4 + 5	6 + 9	7 + 6	3 + 8	9 + 9	5 + 5	4 + 5	7 + 7	1 + 8	7 + 9
1 + 4	4 + 4	7 + 4	3 + 2	2 + 3	3 + 4	9 + 4	8 + 2	5 + 4	6 + 3
3 + 2	4 + 6	9 + 2	6 + 4	8 + 2	4 + 7	2 + 6	5 + 1	9 + 3	7 + 3
6 + 3	2 + 4	5 + 2	1 + 3	9 + 1	7 + 2	2 + 2	4 + 4	6 + 2	2 + 9
1 + 9	3 + 7	3 + 9	8 + 5	7 + 7	7 + 6	3 + 5	6 + 5	5 + 8	8 + 9
2 + 8	4 + 8	3 + 7	8 + 8	7 + 6	3 + 5	9 + 9	5 + 6	7 + 5	9 + 7
3 + 2	4 + 6	9 + 2	6 + 4	8 + 2	4 + 7	2 + 6	5 + 1	9 + 3	7 + 2
7 + 4	6 + 1	8 + 2	3 + 4	9 + 3	5 + 4	4 + 2	2 + 4	1 + 3	6 + 4
3 + 2	4 + 6	9 + 2	6 + 4	8 + 2	4 + 7	2 + 6	5 + 1	9 + 3	7 + 2
6 + 3	2 + 4	5 + 2	1 + 3	9 + 1	7 + 2	2 + 2	4 + 4	6 + 2	2 + 9

Time Test: Mixed

7	6	8	3	9	5	4	2	1	6
+ 4	+ 1	+ 2	+ 4	+ 3	+ 4	+ 2	+ 4	+ 3	+ 4
1	4	7	3	2	3	9	8	5	6
+ 4	+ 4	+ 4	+ 2	+ 3	+ 4	+ 4	+ 2	+ 4	+ 3
3	4	9	6	8	4	2	5	9	7
+ 2	+ 6	+ 2	+ 4	+ 2	+ 7	+ 6	+ 1	+ 3	+ 2
2	4	3	8	6	3	9	5	7	9
+ 8	+ 8	+ 7	+ 8	+ 7	+ 5	+ 9	+ 6	+ 5	+ 7
3	4	9	6	8	4	2	5	9	7
+ 2	+ 6	+ 2	+ 4	+ 2	+ 7	+ 6	+ 1	+ 3	+ 2
4	6	8	3	9	5	4	2	1	6
+ 7	+ 1	+ 2	+ 4	+ 3	+ 4	+ 2	+ 4	+ 3	+ 4
7	5	6	1	3	5	3	8	7	9
+ 6	+ 5	+ 9	+ 7	+ 8	+ 6	+ 5	+ 7	+ 6	+ 5
0	3	8	3	2	5	4	6	6	8
+ 9	+ 8	+ 9	+ 6	+ 5	+ 7	+ 5	+ 9	+ 8	+ 5
7	6	8	3	9	5	4	2	1	6
+ 5	+ 7	+ 6	+ 9	+ 8	+ 7	+ 5	+ 6	+ 8	+ 9
1	4	7	3	2	3	9	8	5	6
+ 8	+ 5	+ 7	+ 8	+ 7	+ 6	+ 9	+ 6	+ 5	+ 7

Time Test: Three Addends

```
   5        8        6        5        8        7        3
   2        2        9        3        7        6        8
 + 3      + 5      + 3      + 5      + 2      + 7      + 4
 ____     ____     ____     ____     ____     ____     ____


   9        6        4        4        8        3        4
   2        5        4        3        4        3        5
 + 3      + 3      + 2      + 9      + 5      + 3      + 3
 ____     ____     ____     ____     ____     ____     ____
```

$6 + 2 + 1 =$ $6 + 5 + 4 =$ $9 + 3 + 0 =$ $8 + 2 + 3 =$ $4 + 4 + 4 =$

$7 + 3 + 6 =$ $4 + 5 + 2 =$ $9 + 1 + 1 =$ $4 + 2 + 8 =$ $1 + 8 + 6 =$

$9 + 0 + 1 =$ $3 + 6 + 5 =$ $8 + 0 + 9 =$ $3 + 1 + 9 =$ $1 + 5 + 9 =$

$5 + 2 + 9 =$ $6 + 5 + 8 =$ $7 + 4 + 2 =$ $8 + 9 + 8 =$ $5 + 2 + 7 =$

```
   7        4        9        6        4        9        3        5
   2        5        1        3        2        0        6        6
 + 1      + 2      + 1      + 6      + 3      + 1      + 5      + 3
 ____     ____     ____     ____     ____     ____     ____     ____


   2        7        7        9        4        8        7        2
   1        0        8        6        4        3        5        1
 + 8      + 9      + 6      + 4      + 7      + 6      + 8      + 9
 ____     ____     ____     ____     ____     ____     ____     ____
```

One- and Two-Digit Addends without Regrouping

Advanced Addition: Practice

44 + 5	31 + 3	14 + 4	53 + 3	82 + 6	91 + 8	14 + 3	61 + 6	31 + 8	12 + 3
35 + 2	56 + 3	60 + 4	52 + 5	21 + 6	18 + 1	73 + 3	41 + 6	52 + 3	16 + 2
54 + 2	81 + 3	32 + 4	22 + 7	61 + 8	70 + 1	25 + 2	72 + 4	27 + 2	36 + 2
62 + 5	72 + 4	51 + 6	36 + 3	52 + 7	62 + 6	38 + 1	53 + 5	62 + 3	33 + 6
44 + 2	61 + 5	18 + 1	21 + 6	20 + 3	43 + 6	25 + 4	62 + 4	71 + 8	52 + 6
55 + 3	73 + 6	81 + 4	16 + 2	23 + 6	77 + 2	33 + 2	42 + 4	21 + 8	36 + 2

Two-Digit Addends without Regrouping

55 + 13	73 + 21	89 + 10	16 + 12	23 + 16	77 + 12	16 + 22	14 + 34	21 + 28	36 + 10
21 + 38	10 + 19	14 + 35	11 + 87	40 + 18	48 + 11	61 + 20	71 + 38	12 + 47	11 + 18
18 + 11	20 + 10	13 + 25	13 + 21	25 + 14	84 + 10	52 + 16	47 + 12	63 + 15	12 + 12
31 + 38	16 + 12	23 + 25	87 + 12	45 + 14	36 + 41	26 + 31	19 + 40	14 + 44	29 + 10
66 + 31	41 + 18	33 + 32	58 + 71	19 + 10	63 + 23	24 + 81	37 + 12	18 + 11	22 + 14
34 + 14	61 + 17	72 + 22	18 + 31	48 + 11	52 + 27	66 + 13	32 + 24	12 + 17	80 + 18

Two-Digit Addends with Regrouping

| 66
+ 39 | 47
+ 18 | 39
+ 32 | 58
+76 | 83
+ 18 | 59
+ 56 | 49
+ 81 | 37
+ 18 | 18
+ 23 | 22
+ 29 |

| 34
+ 17 | 68
+ 17 | 79
+ 22 | 18
+ 39 | 48
+ 17 | 52
+ 69 | 66
+ 28 | 39
+ 24 | 48
+ 19 | 86
+ 18 |

| 69
+ 16 | 75
+ 25 | 82
+ 38 | 26
+ 37 | 71
+ 89 | 63
+ 39 | 19
+ 62 | 18
+ 32 | 16
+ 48 | 44
+ 47 |

| 32
+ 38 | 43
+ 29 | 57
+ 63 | 61
+ 59 | 43
+ 18 | 66
+ 76 | 12
+ 39 | 59
+ 22 | 23
+ 18 | 33
+ 38 |

| 62
+ 49 | 53
+ 38 | 56
+ 45 | 92
+ 19 | 83
+ 29 | 19
+ 81 | 21
+ 69 | 57
+ 37 | 60
+ 40 | 38
+ 23 |

| 55
+ 38 | 54
+ 68 | 57
+ 44 | 19
+ 33 | 63
+ 38 | 61
+ 59 | 18
+ 23 | 23
+ 48 | 81
+ 99 | 59
+ 46 |

285 + 186	849 + 132	659 + 167	135 + 238	294 + 438
395 + 167	871 + 158	603 + 232	590 + 287	257 + 129
789 + 124	732 + 365	135 + 139	209 + 367	587 + 496
179 + 524	236 + 122	841 + 163	294 + 158	145 + 339
651 + 175	852 + 446	189 + 356	146 + 349	177 + 194
369 + 691	582 + 230	112 + 260	271 + 289	177 + 555

Mixed Addition

6 + 3	2 + 4	5 + 2	1 + 3	9 + 1	7 + 2	2 + 2	4 + 4

49 + 17	68 + 44	97 + 13	49 + 32	23 + 48	77 + 16	88 + 22	57 + 34

55 + 6	73 + 8	89 + 4	16 + 6	23 + 8	77 + 7	39 + 2	48 + 4

221 + 168	301 + 589	227 + 168	146 + 349	177 + 194	651 + 175	852 + 446	189 + 356

$7 + 3 + 6 =$ $4 + 5 + 2 =$ $9 + 1 + 1 =$ $4 + 2 + 8 =$ $1 + 8 + 6 =$

$9 + 0 + 1 =$ $3 + 6 + 5 =$ $8 + 0 + 9 =$ $3 + 1 + 9 =$ $1 + 5 + 9 =$

1 + 9	3 + 7	3 + 9	8 + 5	7 + 7	7 + 6	3 + 5	6 + 5

Mixed Addition

395	871	603	590	257	789	732	135
+ 167	+ 158	+ 232	+ 287	+ 129	+ 124	+ 365	+ 139

62	72	51	36	52	62	38	53
+ 5	+ 4	+ 6	+ 3	+ 7	+ 6	+ 1	+ 5

44	61	18	21	20	43	25	62
+ 2	+ 5	+ 1	+ 6	+ 3	+ 6	+ 4	+ 4

6 + 2 + 1 =   6 + 5 + 4 =   9 + 3 + 0 =   8 + 2 + 3 =   4 + 4 + 4 =

5 + 2 + 9 =   6 + 5 + 8 =   7 + 4 + 2 =   8 + 9 + 8 =   5 + 2 + 7 =

7	6	8	3	9	5	4	2
+ 4	+ 1	+ 2	+ 4	+ 3	+ 4	+ 2	+ 4

3	4	9	6	8	4	2	5
+ 2	+ 6	+ 2	+ 4	+ 2	+ 7	+ 6	+ 1

CRISS Addition Game

Carefully cut apart all the tiles on pages 89 – 93. Place the equal signs (=) and the plus signs (+) in separate piles. Players can use as many of these as they need. Place all the remaining tiles in a bag or face down on the table. Each player draws 10 tiles and places them faceup on the table.

The first player places tiles from his or her pile on the table to create an addition sentence. Draw 3 more tiles from the draw pile. For example:

$$2 + 6 = 8$$

The player to the left goes next. This player makes a new addition sentence, using one of the tiles from the first sentence. For example: 6 + 3 = 9.

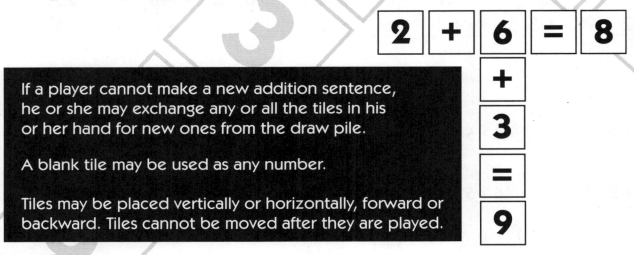

If a player cannot make a new addition sentence, he or she may exchange any or all the tiles in his or her hand for new ones from the draw pile.

A blank tile may be used as any number.

Tiles may be placed vertically or horizontally, forward or backward. Tiles cannot be moved after they are played.

Scoring: Players score the sum of their addition sentence. Therefore, players should study the field carefully and place tiles with the greatest sum. Play continues until one player reaches a predetermined number of points or until no additional cards can be played. The winner is the player with the most points.

- Place the first addition sentence in the center of the table, allowing for plenty of room to play.
- Decide ahead of time whether or not to allow addition sentences with addends 10 or higher. For example: 10 + 5 = 15
- Decide ahead of time whether or not to allow 3 or more addend addition sentences. For example: 2 + 1 + 4 = 7

CrissCross Addition Game

1	1	1	1	1	1	1
2	2	2	2	2	2	2
3	3	3	3	3	3	3
4	4	4	4	4	4	4
5	5	5	5	5	5	5
6	6	6	6	6	6	6
7	7	7	7	7	7	7
8	8	8	8	8	8	8
9	9	9	9	9	9	9

This page was intentionally left blank for the "CrissCross Addition" Game to be completed.

CrissCross Addition Game

10	10	10	10	11	11	12
12	12	13	13	14	14	15
15	16	16	17	18	0	0
0	0					
=	=	=	=	=	=	=
=	=	=	=	=	=	=
=	=	=	=	=	=	=
=	=	=	=	=	=	=
=	=	=	=	=	=	=

This page was intentionally left blank for the "CrissCross Addition" Game to be completed.

CrissCross Addition Game

=	=	=	=	=	=	=
=	=	=	=	=	=	=
+	+	+	+	+	+	+
+	+	+	+	+	+	+
+	+	+	+	+	+	+
+	+	+	+	+	+	+
+	+	+	+	+	+	+
+	+	+	+	+	+	+
+	+	+	+	+	+	+

This page was intentionally left blank for the "CrissCross Addition" Game to be completed.

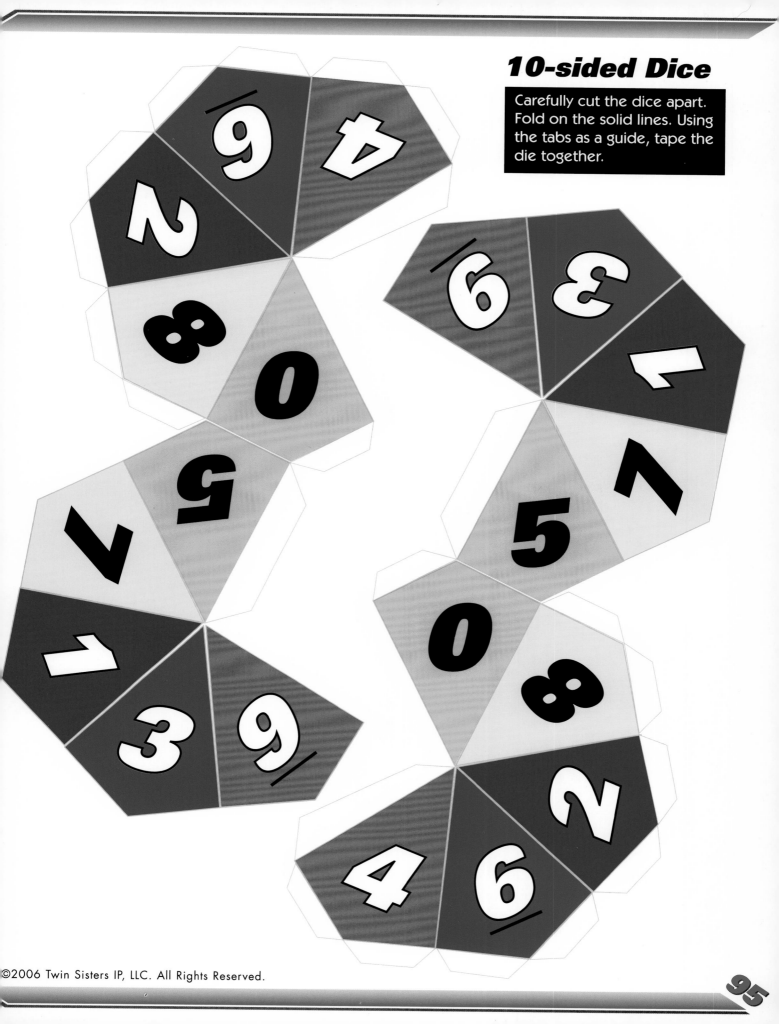

10-sided Dice

Carefully cut the dice apart. Fold on the solid lines. Using the tabs as a guide, tape the die together.

This page was intentionally left blank for the 10-sided Die to be completed.